2023-2024

Monthly Planner

THIS BOOK BELONGS TO:

____

Personal Information

Name: ____________________

Address: ____________________

City: ____________________ State: ____________________

Phone: ____________________

Email: ____________________

Emergency Contacts

Name: ____________________

Relationship: ____________________

Phone: ____________________

Email: ____________________

Name: ____________________

Relationship: ____________________

Phone: ____________________

Email: ____________________

Doctor: ____________________

Phone: ____________________

Email: ____________________

Doctor: ____________________

Phone: ____________________

Email: ____________________

Other

____

____

____

____

Contacts

Name:

Address:

Phone:

Email:

Name:

Address:

Phone:

Email:

Name:

Address:

Phone:

Email:

Name:

Address:

Phone:

Email:

Name:

Address:

Phone:

Email:

Name:

Address:

Phone:

Email:

Name:

Address:

Phone:

Email:

Name:

Address:

Phone:

Email:

Contacts

Name:____________________ Name:____________________

Address:__________________ Address:__________________

Phone:____________________ Phone:____________________

Email: ____________________ Email: ____________________

Name:____________________ Name:____________________

Address:__________________ Address:__________________

Phone:____________________ Phone:____________________

Email: ____________________ Email: ____________________

Name:____________________ Name:____________________

Address:__________________ Address:__________________

Phone:____________________ Phone:____________________

Email: ____________________ Email: ____________________

Name:____________________ Name:____________________

Address:__________________ Address:__________________

Phone:____________________ Phone:____________________

Email: ____________________ Email: ____________________

Password Log

Website:

Username:____________________________

Password:____________________________

Email Linked:__________________________

Membership Expiration Date:____________

Notes:_______________________________

Website:

Username:____________________________

Password:____________________________

Email Linked:__________________________

Membership Expiration Date:____________

Notes:_______________________________

Website:

Username:____________________________

Password:____________________________

Email Linked:__________________________

Membership Expiration Date:____________

Notes:_______________________________

Website:

Username:____________________________

Password:____________________________

Email Linked:__________________________

Membership Expiration Date:____________

Notes:_______________________________

Website:

Username:____________________________

Password:____________________________

Email Linked:__________________________

Membership Expiration Date:____________

Notes:_______________________________

Website:

Username:____________________________

Password:____________________________

Email Linked:__________________________

Membership Expiration Date:____________

Notes:_______________________________

Website:

Username:____________________________

Password:____________________________

Email Linked:__________________________

Membership Expiration Date:____________

Notes:_______________________________

Website:

Username:____________________________

Password:____________________________

Email Linked:__________________________

Membership Expiration Date:____________

Notes:_______________________________

Password Log

Website:

Username:________________________

Password:________________________

Email Linked:________________________

Membership Expiration Date:____________

Notes:________________________

Website:

Username:________________________

Password:________________________

Email Linked:________________________

Membership Expiration Date:____________

Notes:________________________

Website:

Username:________________________

Password:________________________

Email Linked:________________________

Membership Expiration Date:____________

Notes:________________________

Website:

Username:________________________

Password:________________________

Email Linked:________________________

Membership Expiration Date:____________

Notes:________________________

Website:

Username:________________________

Password:________________________

Email Linked:________________________

Membership Expiration Date:____________

Notes:________________________

Website:

Username:________________________

Password:________________________

Email Linked:________________________

Membership Expiration Date:____________

Notes:________________________

Website:

Username:________________________

Password:________________________

Email Linked:________________________

Membership Expiration Date:____________

Notes:________________________

Website:

Username:________________________

Password:________________________

Email Linked:________________________

Membership Expiration Date:____________

Notes:________________________

Year in Review

January 2023

S	M	T	W	T	F	S
1	2	3	4	5	6	7
8	9	10	11	12	13	14
15	16	17	18	19	20	21
22	23	24	25	26	27	28
29	30	31				

○:6 ◑:14 ●:21 ◐:28

February 2023

S	M	T	W	T	F	S
			1	2	3	4
5	6	7	8	9	10	11
12	13	14	15	16	17	18
19	20	21	22	23	24	25
26	27	28				

○:5 ◑:13 ●:20 ◐:27

March 2023

S	M	T	W	T	F	S
			1	2	3	4
5	6	7	8	9	10	11
12	13	14	15	16	17	18
19	20	21	22	23	24	25
26	27	28	29	30	31	

○:7 ◑:14 ●:21 ◐:28

April 2023

S	M	T	W	T	F	S
						1
2	3	4	5	6	7	8
9	10	11	12	13	14	15
16	17	18	19	20	21	22
23	24	25	26	27	28	29
30						

○:6 ◑:13 ●:20 ◐:27

May 2023

S	M	T	W	T	F	S
	1	2	3	4	5	6
7	8	9	10	11	12	13
14	15	16	17	18	19	20
21	22	23	24	25	26	27
28	29	30	31			

○:5 ◑:12 ●:19 ◐:27

June 2023

S	M	T	W	T	F	S
				1	2	3
4	5	6	7	8	9	10
11	12	13	14	15	16	17
18	19	20	21	22	23	24
25	26	27	28	29	30	

○:3 ◑:10 ●:18 ◐:26

July 2023

S	M	T	W	T	F	S
						1
2	3	4	5	6	7	8
9	10	11	12	13	14	15
16	17	18	19	20	21	22
23	24	25	26	27	28	29
30	31					

○:3 ◑:9 ●:17 ◐:25

August 2023

S	M	T	W	T	F	S
		1	2	3	4	5
6	7	8	9	10	11	12
13	14	15	16	17	18	19
20	21	22	23	24	25	26
27	28	29	30	31		

○:1 ◑:8 ●:16 ◐:24 ○:30

September 2023

S	M	T	W	T	F	S
					1	2
3	4	5	6	7	8	9
10	11	12	13	14	15	16
17	18	19	20	21	22	23
24	25	26	27	28	29	30

◑:6 ●:14 ◐:22 ○:29

October 2023

S	M	T	W	T	F	S
1	2	3	4	5	6	7
8	9	10	11	12	13	14
15	16	17	18	19	20	21
22	23	24	25	26	27	28
29	30	31				

◑:6 ●:14 ◐:21 ○:28

November 2023

S	M	T	W	T	F	S
			1	2	3	4
5	6	7	8	9	10	11
12	13	14	15	16	17	18
19	20	21	22	23	24	25
26	27	28	29	30		

◑:5 ●:13 ◐:20 ○:27

December 2023

S	M	T	W	T	F	S
					1	2
3	4	5	6	7	8	9
10	11	12	13	14	15	16
17	18	19	20	21	22	23
24	25	26	27	28	29	30
31						

◑:5 ●:12 ◐:19 ○:26

Holidays & Celebrations

Jan 1	New Year's Day
Jan 2	New Year's Day (observed)
Jan 16	Martin Luther King Jr. Day
Feb 14	Valentine's Day
Feb 20	Presidents' Day
Mar 17	St. Patrick's Day
Apr 9	Easter Sunday
Apr 18	Tax Day
May 5	Cinco de Mayo
May 14	Mother's Day
May 29	Memorial Day
Jun 18	Father's Day
Jun 19	Juneteenth
Jul 4	Independence Day
Sep 4	Labor Day
Oct 9	Columbus Day
Oct 31	Halloween
Nov 10	Veterans Day (Observed)
Nov 11	Veterans Day
Nov 23	Thanksgiving Day
Nov 24	Black Friday
Dec 24	Christmas Eve
Dec 25	Christmas Day
Dec 31	New Year's Eve

Notes

Important Dates

January 2023

February 2023

March 2023

April 2023

May 2023

June 2023

July 2023

August 2023

September 2023

October 2023

November 2023

December 2023

Notes

January 2023

SUNDAY	MONDAY	TUESDAY	WEDNESDAY
1 New Year's Day	2 New Year's Day (Observed)	3	4
8	9	10	11
15	16 Martin Luther King Jr. Day	17	18
22	23	24	25
29	30	31	

"No mistake or failure is as bad as to stop and not try again."
- John Wanamaker

THURSDAY	FRIDAY	SATURDAY
5	6	7
12	13	14
19	20	21
26	27	28

NOTES

February 2023

SUNDAY	MONDAY	TUESDAY	WEDNESDAY
			1
5	6	7	8
12	13	14 Valentine's Day	15
19	20 President's Day	21	22
26	27	28	

" You will never find time for anything. If you want time you must make it. "

- Charles Buxton

THURSDAY	FRIDAY	SATURDAY
2	3	4
9	10	11
16	17	18
23	24	25

NOTES

March 2023

SUNDAY	MONDAY	TUESDAY	WEDNESDAY
			1
5	6	7	8
12	13	14	15
19	20	21	22
26	27	28	29

" Do not spoil what you have by desiring what you have not; remember that what you now have was once among the things you only hoped for. " - Epicurus

THURSDAY	FRIDAY	SATURDAY
2	3	4
9	10	11
16	17 St Patrick's Day	18
23	24	25
30	31	

NOTES

April 2023

SUNDAY	MONDAY	TUESDAY	WEDNESDAY
2	3	4	5
9 Easter Sunday	10	11	12
16	17	18 Tax Day	19
23 / 30	24	25	26

“ Nothing is impossible to a willing heart. ”
- John Heywood

THURSDAY	FRIDAY	SATURDAY
		1
6	7	8
13	14	15
20	21	22
27	28	29

NOTES

May 2023

SUNDAY	MONDAY	TUESDAY	WEDNESDAY
	1	2	3
7	8	9	10
14 Mother's Day	15	16	17
21	22	23	24
28	29 Memorial Day	30	31

“ The secret of change is to focus all your energy not on fighting the old but on building the new. ” - Socrates

THURSDAY	FRIDAY	SATURDAY
4	5 Cinco De Mayo	6
11	12	13
18	19	20
25	26	27

NOTES

June 2023

SUNDAY	MONDAY	TUESDAY	WEDNESDAY
4	5	6	7
11	12	13	14
18 Father's Day	19 Juneteenth	20	21
25	26	27	28

" Success is a science; if you have the conditions, you get the result. "

- Oscar Wilde

THURSDAY	FRIDAY	SATURDAY
1	2	3
8	9	10
15	16	17
22	23	24
29	30	

NOTES

July 2023

SUNDAY	MONDAY	TUESDAY	WEDNESDAY
2	3	4 Independence Day	5
9	10	11	12
16	17	18	19
23 / 30	24 / 31	25	26

" Most of the shadows of life are caused by standing in our own sunshine. "

- Ralph Waldo Emerson

THURSDAY	FRIDAY	SATURDAY
		1
6	7	8
13	14	15
20	21	22
27	28	29

NOTES

August 2023

SUNDAY	MONDAY	TUESDAY	WEDNESDAY
		1	2
6	7	8	9
13	14	15	16
20	21	22	23
27	28	29	30

" An action committed in anger is an action doomed to failure. "

- Genghis Khan

THURSDAY	FRIDAY	SATURDAY
3	4	5
10	11	12
17	18	19
24	25	26
31		

NOTES

September 2023

SUNDAY	MONDAY	TUESDAY	WEDNESDAY
3	4 Labor Day	5	6
10	11	12	13
17	18	19	20
24	25	26	27

" Concentrate all your thoughts upon the work at hand. The sun's rays do not burn until brought to focus. "
- Alexander Graham Bell

THURSDAY	FRIDAY	SATURDAY
	1	2
7	8	9
14	15	16
21	22	23
28	29	30

NOTES

October 2023

SUNDAY	MONDAY	TUESDAY	WEDNESDAY
1	2	3	4
8	9 Columbus Day	10	11
15	16	17	18
22	23	24	25
29	30	31 Halloween	

“ If you correct your mind, the rest of your life will fall into place. ”

- Lao Tzu

THURSDAY	FRIDAY	SATURDAY
5	6	7
12	13	14
19	20	21
26	27	28

NOTES

November 2023

SUNDAY	MONDAY	TUESDAY	WEDNESDAY
			1
5	6	7	8
12	13	14	15
19	20	21	22
26	27	28	29

"Rule your mind or it will rule you."

- Horace

THURSDAY	FRIDAY	SATURDAY
2	3	4
9	10 Veterans Day (Observed)	11 Veterans Day
16	17	18
23 Thanksgiving Day	24 Black Friday	25
30		

NOTES

December 2023

SUNDAY	MONDAY	TUESDAY	WEDNESDAY
3	4	5	6
10	11	12	13
17	18	19	20
Christmas Eve 24 / New Year's Eve 31	25 Christmas Day	26	27

" Cultivate the habit of being grateful for every good thing that comes to you and to give thanks continuously. And because all things have contributed to your advancement, you should include all things in your gratitude. "

- Ralph Waldo Emerson

THURSDAY	FRIDAY	SATURDAY
	1	2
7	8	9
14	15	16
21	22	23
28	29	30

NOTES

Year in Review

January 2024

S	M	T	W	T	F	S
	1	2	3	4	5	6
7	8	9	10	11	12	13
14	15	16	17	18	19	20
21	22	23	24	25	26	27
28	29	30	31			

◑:3 ●:11 ◐:17 ○:25

February 2024

S	M	T	W	T	F	S
				1	2	3
4	5	6	7	8	9	10
11	12	13	14	15	16	17
18	19	20	21	22	23	24
25	26	27	28	29		

◑:2 ●:9 ◐:16 ○:24

March 2024

S	M	T	W	T	F	S
					1	2
3	4	5	6	7	8	9
10	11	12	13	14	15	16
17	18	19	20	21	22	23
24	25	26	27	28	29	30
31						

◑:3 ●:10 ◐:17 ○:25

April 2024

S	M	T	W	T	F	S
	1	2	3	4	5	6
7	8	9	10	11	12	13
14	15	16	17	18	19	20
21	22	23	24	25	26	27
28	29	30				

◑:1 ●:8 ◐:15 ○:23

May 2024

S	M	T	W	T	F	S
			1	2	3	4
5	6	7	8	9	10	11
12	13	14	15	16	17	18
19	20	21	22	23	24	25
26	27	28	29	30	31	

◑:1 ●:7 ◐:15 ○:23 ◑:30

June 2024

S	M	T	W	T	F	S
						1
2	3	4	5	6	7	8
9	10	11	12	13	14	15
16	17	18	19	20	21	22
23	24	25	26	27	28	29
30						

●:6 ◐:14 ○:21 ◑:28

July 2024

S	M	T	W	T	F	S
	1	2	3	4	5	6
7	8	9	10	11	12	13
14	15	16	17	18	19	20
21	22	23	24	25	26	27
28	29	30	31			

●:5 ◐:13 ○:21 ◑:27

August 2024

S	M	T	W	T	F	S
				1	2	3
4	5	6	7	8	9	10
11	12	13	14	15	16	17
18	19	20	21	22	23	24
25	26	27	28	29	30	31

●:4 ◐:12 ○:19 ◑:26

September 2024

S	M	T	W	T	F	S
1	2	3	4	5	6	7
8	9	10	11	12	13	14
15	16	17	18	19	20	21
22	23	24	25	26	27	28
29	30					

●:2 ◐:11 ○:17 ◑:24

October 2024

S	M	T	W	T	F	S
		1	2	3	4	5
6	7	8	9	10	11	12
13	14	15	16	17	18	19
20	21	22	23	24	25	26
27	28	29	30	31		

●:2 ◐:10 ○:17 ◑:24

November 2024

S	M	T	W	T	F	S
					1	2
3	4	5	6	7	8	9
10	11	12	13	14	15	16
17	18	19	20	21	22	23
24	25	26	27	28	29	30

●:1 ◐:9 ○:15 ◑:22

December 2024

S	M	T	W	T	F	S
1	2	3	4	5	6	7
8	9	10	11	12	13	14
15	16	17	18	19	20	21
22	23	24	25	26	27	28
29	30	31				

●:1 ◐:8 ○:15 ◑:22 ●:30

Holidays & Celebrations

Jan 1	New Year's Day
Jan 15	Martin Luther King Jr. Day
Feb 14	Valentine's Day
Feb 19	Presidents' Day
Mar 17	St. Patrick's Day
Mar 31	Easter Sunday
Apr 15	Tax Day
May 5	Cinco de Mayo
May 12	Mother's Day
May 27	Memorial Day
Jun 16	Father's Day
Jun 19	Juneteenth
Jul 4	Independence Day
Sep 2	Labor Day
Oct 14	Columbus Day
Oct 31	Halloween
Nov 11	Veterans Day
Nov 28	Thanksgiving Day
Nov 29	Black Friday
Dec 24	Christmas Eve
Dec 25	Christmas Day
Dec 31	New Year's Eve

Notes

Important Dates

January 2024

February 2024

March 2024

April 2024

May 2024

June 2024

July 2024

August 2024

September 2024

October 2024

November 2024

December 2024

Notes

January 2024

SUNDAY	MONDAY	TUESDAY	WEDNESDAY
	1 New Year's Day	2	3
7	8	9	10
14	15 Martin Luther King Jr. Day	16	17
21	22	23	24
28	29	30	31

" Luck is what happens when preparation meets opportunity. "
- Lucius Annaeus Seneca

THURSDAY	FRIDAY	SATURDAY
4	5	6
11	12	13
18	19	20
25	26	27

NOTES

February 2024

SUNDAY	MONDAY	TUESDAY	WEDNESDAY
4	5	6	7
11	12	13	14 Valentine's Day
18	19 President's Day	20	21
25	26	27	28

" Do your little bit of good where you are; it's those little bits of good put together that overwhelm the world. "

- Desmond Tutu

THURSDAY	FRIDAY	SATURDAY
1	2	3
8	9	10
15	16	17
22	23	24
29		

NOTES

March 2024

SUNDAY	MONDAY	TUESDAY	WEDNESDAY
3	4	5	6
10	11	12	13
17 St Patrick's Day	18	19	20
24 Easter Sunday 31	25	26	27

" Whatever you think you can do or believe you can do, begin it.
Action has magic, grace, and power in it. " - Johann Wolfgang von Goethe

THURSDAY	FRIDAY	SATURDAY
	1	2
7	8	9
14	15	16
21	22	23
28	29	30

NOTES

April 2024

SUNDAY	MONDAY	TUESDAY	WEDNESDAY
	1	2	3
7	8	9	10
14	15 Tax day	16	17
21	22	23	24
28	29	30	

" Every failure is a step to success. "

- William Whewell

THURSDAY	FRIDAY	SATURDAY
4	5	6
11	12	13
18	19	20
25	26	27

NOTES

May 2024

SUNDAY	MONDAY	TUESDAY	WEDNESDAY
			1
5 Cinco De Mayo	6	7	8
12 Mother's Day	13	14	15
19	20	21	22
26	27 Memorial Day	28	29

" I'm a great believer in luck and I find the harder I work, the more I have of it. "

- Thomas Jefferson

THURSDAY	FRIDAY	SATURDAY
2	3	4
9	10	11
16	17	18
23	24	25
30	31	

NOTES

June 2024

SUNDAY	MONDAY	TUESDAY	WEDNESDAY
2	3	4	5
9	10	11	12
16 Father's Day	17	18	19 Juneteenth
23 / 30	24	25	26

" To be alive— is Power. "

- Emily Dickinson

THURSDAY	FRIDAY	SATURDAY
		1
6	7	8
13	14	15
20	21	22
27	28	29

NOTES

July 2024

SUNDAY	MONDAY	TUESDAY	WEDNESDAY
	1	2	3
7	8	9	10
14	15	16	17
21	22	23	24
28	29	30	31

"I like the dreams of the future better than the history of the past"
- Thomas Jefferson

THURSDAY	FRIDAY	SATURDAY
4 Independence Day	5	6
11	12	13
18	19	20
25	26	27

NOTES

August 2024

SUNDAY	MONDAY	TUESDAY	WEDNESDAY
4	5	6	7
11	12	13	14
18	19	20	21
25	26	27	28

" The grand essentials of happiness are: something to do, something to love, and something to hope for. " - Joseph Addison

THURSDAY	FRIDAY	SATURDAY
1	2	3
8	9	10
15	16	17
22	23	24
29	30	31

NOTES

September 2024

SUNDAY	MONDAY	TUESDAY	WEDNESDAY
1	2 Labor day	3	4
8	9	10	11
15	16	17	18
22	23	24	25
29	30		

" When you doubt your power, you give power to your doubt. "
- Honoré de Balzac

THURSDAY	FRIDAY	SATURDAY
5	6	7
12	13	14
19	20	21
26	27	28

NOTES

October 2024

SUNDAY	MONDAY	TUESDAY	WEDNESDAY
		1	2
6	7	8	9
13	14 Columbus Day	15	16
20	21	22	23
27	28	29	30

" While there's life, there's hope. "

- Marcus Tullius Cicero

THURSDAY	FRIDAY	SATURDAY
3	4	5
10	11	12
17	18	19
24	25	26
31 Halloween		

NOTES

November 2024

SUNDAY	MONDAY	TUESDAY	WEDNESDAY
3	4	5	6
10	11 Veterans Day	12	13
17	18	19	20
24	25	26	27

" The best way to predict your future is to create it. "
- Abraham Lincoln

THURSDAY	FRIDAY	SATURDAY
	1	2
7	8	9
14	15	16
21	22	23
28 Thanksgiving Day	29 Black Friday	30

NOTES

December 2024

SUNDAY	MONDAY	TUESDAY	WEDNESDAY
1	2	3	4
8	9	10	11
15	16	17	18
22	23	24 Christmas Eve	25 Christmas Day
29	30	31 New Year's Eve	

" Twenty years from now you will be more disappointed by the things that you didn't do than by the ones you did do, so throw off the bowlines, sail away from safe harbor, catch the trade winds in your sails. Explore, Dream, Discover. "

- Mark Twain

THURSDAY	FRIDAY	SATURDAY
5	6	7
12	13	14
19	20	21
26	27	28

NOTES

Notes

Notes

We'd like to know what you think!

If you liked this planner, please support us by leaving a review on Amazon! Your kind reviews and comments will encourage us to make more planners like this.

Made in the USA
Monee, IL
23 March 2023

30399166R00063